Another Wo~ (Un Autre Monde) Coloring Book

Copyright © 2016 Hawaiian Heritage Press

Hawaiian Heritage Press

ISBN-13: 978-1-943476-34-3

Jean Ignace Isidore Gérard (1803-1847) was a French artist and satirist who was known by his pseudonym, J. J. Grandville. *Un Autre Monde* (Another World), published in 1844, was a highly original work, its surreal illustrations veering from whimsical to nightmarish. This coloring book contains thirty-two high-resolution reproductions of the original illustrations.

Portrait by Émile Lassalle(1840)

Name:

Date:

Notes:

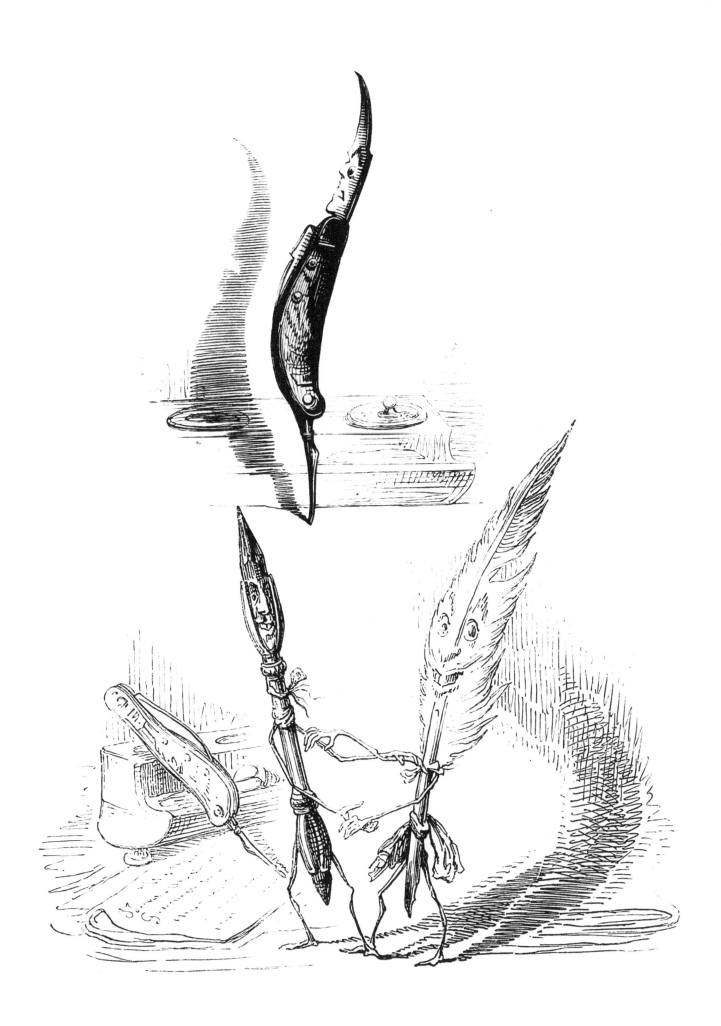

Name:

Date:

Notes:

Name:

Date:

Notes:

Name:

Date:

Notes:

Name:

Date:

Notes:

Name:

Date:

Notes:

CONCERT A LA VAPEUR.

Name:

Date:

Notes:

Mlle TENDER ET M. TUNNEL

Dans le diurne : Rive gauche et Rive droite

ha ha   ha ha
ha ha ha   ha ha ha

ha   ha   ha
ha ha ha   ha   ha

ah
ah   ah ah

oh la la la la ! oh ah ! oh ah !

Name:

Date:

Notes:

Des mesures sont prises pour qu'un pareil accident ne se renouvelle plus.

Name:

Date:

Notes:

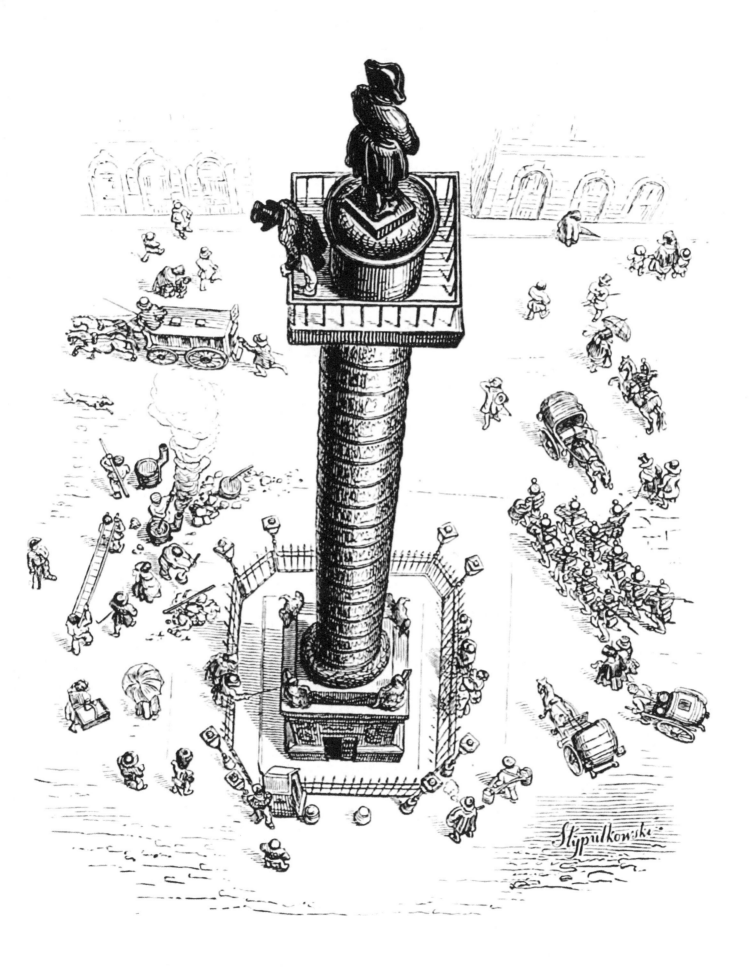

Name:

Date:

Notes:

Name:

Date:

Notes:

1. Lièvre faisandé.
2. Oie en matelotte.
3. Homard saumonné.
4. Perdreau à queue d'écrevisse.

5. Bécasse crapaudine.
6. Sarcelle en brochet.
7. Escargot-tortue.
8. Grenouille tartare.

9. Hure de poularde truffée.
10. Cochon-dinde rôti.
11. Canard aux olives.
12. Chevreuil à la crête de coq.

Name:

Date:

Notes:

Name:

Date:

Notes:

BAL MASQUÉ.

Name:

Date:

Notes:

Dandysme et pétrin   Grandisson-Macaire.   Bases diplomatiques.

Conviction et Arlequinade.   La morale d'aujourd'hui.   Notre-Dame de Lorette et l'Opéra.

Name:

Date:

Notes:

APOCALYPSE DU BALLET.

Name:

Date:

Notes:

Name:

Date:

Notes:

LE RÉVEIL DES PLANTES.

Name:

Date:

Notes:

LES POISSONS D'AVRIL.

Name:

Date:

Notes:

Name:

Date:

Notes:

Name:

Date:

Notes:

Name:
Date:
Notes:

Name:
Date:
Notes:

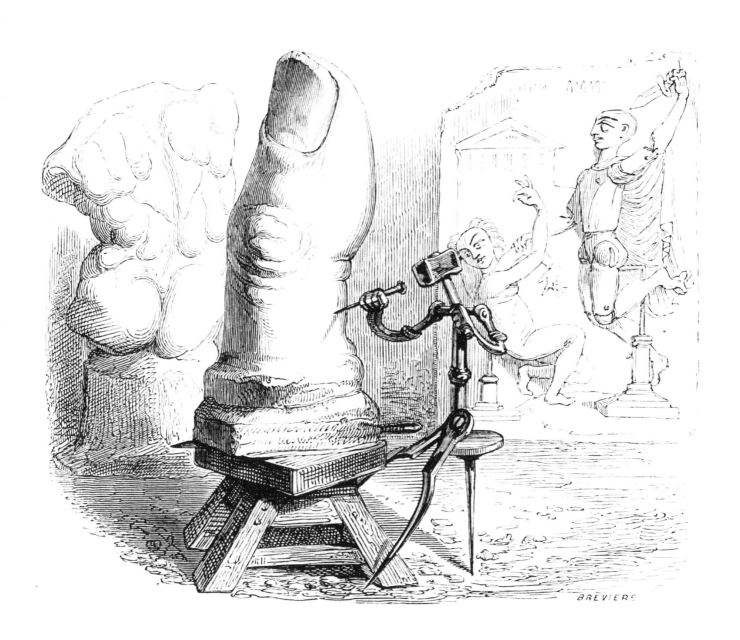

Voilà pour la critique impartiale.

Name:
Date:
Notes:

UNE ÉCLIPSE CONJUGALE.

Name:
Date:
Notes:

PÉRÉGRINATIONS D'UNE COMÈTE.

Name:
Date:
Notes:

LE PERCHOIR.

Name:
Date:
Notes:

Name:
Date:
Notes:

L'ÉVENTAIL D'IRIS,

Name:
Date:
Notes:

Mlle LEUCOTHOÉ. — ROLE DE PHÈDRE.

Name:
Date:
Notes:

LES GRANDS HOMMES AUX CHAMPS-ÉLYSÉES.

Name:
Date:
Notes:

Name:

Date:

Notes:

Hawaiian Heritage Press

Hawai`i's finest classic and modern literature.

HawaiianHeritage.org

Sign up to learn about events, promotions and new releases

bit.ly/HawaiianHeritage

Made in the USA
Monee, IL
31 March 2021